Come look in the cave!
These five bats hide here.

Come look in the den!
This fox can make its home here.

Come look in the shade!

These big cats ate.

They like to bite on a bone.

Come look in this big case!
These five snakes like to doze
in the sun.

Come look in the pool!
More cubs will use the pool too.

Come look at the hill!
These nine ants make a nest.

Come look in the pen!
These two apes ate and
made a mess.

We came in that bus.

Is it time to go home?